ARE YOU SMARTER THAN A 5TH GRADER

Can you make the grade?

TAKE A QUIZ!

bendon

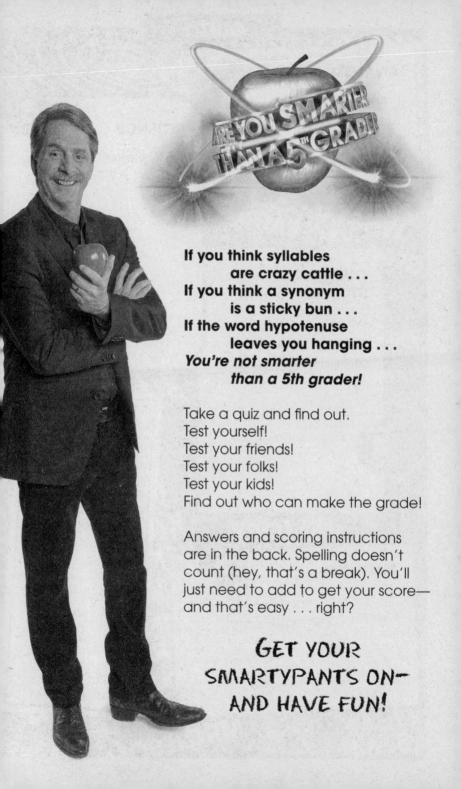

**If you think syllables
     are crazy cattle . . .
If you think a synonym
     is a sticky bun . . .
If the word hypotenuse
     leaves you hanging . . .
*You're not smarter
     than a 5th grader!***

Take a quiz and find out.
Test yourself!
Test your friends!
Test your folks!
Test your kids!
Find out who can make the grade!

Answers and scoring instructions
are in the back. Spelling doesn't
count (hey, that's a break). You'll
just need to add to get your score—
and that's easy . . . right?

GET YOUR
SMARTYPANTS ON—
AND HAVE FUN!

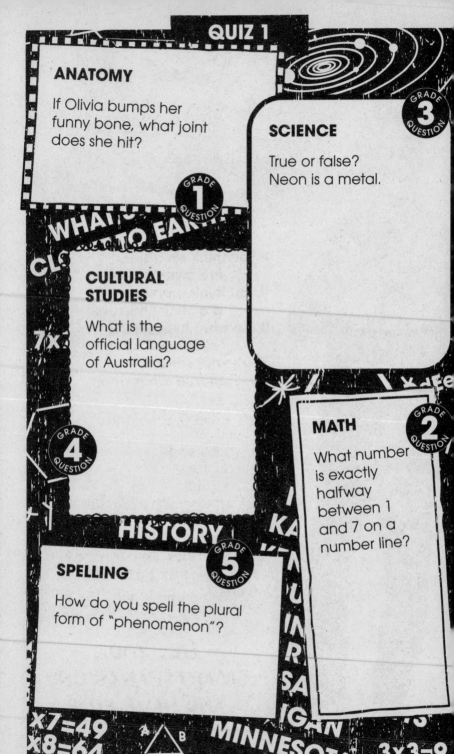

QUIZ 1

ANATOMY

If Olivia bumps her funny bone, what joint does she hit?

GRADE 1 QUESTION

SCIENCE

True or false? Neon is a metal.

GRADE 3 QUESTION

CULTURAL STUDIES

What is the official language of Australia?

GRADE 4 QUESTION

MATH

What number is exactly halfway between 1 and 7 on a number line?

GRADE 2 QUESTION

SPELLING

How do you spell the plural form of "phenomenon"?

GRADE 5 QUESTION

MATH

GRADE 3 QUESTION

How many multiples of 8 fall between 14 and 25?

SCIENCE

GRADE 5 QUESTION

What is the most abundant element in the universe?

ENGLISH

GRADE 1 QUESTION

What is missing from this sentence

ART

GRADE 4 QUESTION

Georgia O'Keeffe, renowned painter of flowers and landscapes, was born in what country?

U.S. STUDIES

GRADE 2 QUESTION

The oriole is the official bird of what U.S. state?

GRADE 1 QUESTION

MUSIC

True or false? A cello is larger in size than a viola.

GRADE 4 QUESTION

ENGLISH

What is the preposition in:
Man has walked on the moon.

GRADE 5 QUESTION

CULTURAL STUDIES

The Nobel Peace Prize is presented annually in what country?

ANATOMY

GRADE 2 QUESTION

True or false?
The human shoulder is a ball-and-socket joint.

GRADE 3 QUESTION

SCIENCE

True or false?
Salt is a mineral.

QUIZ 4

ART

Which adhesive is usually used for papier-mâché?
A) candle wax
B) paste
C) tape

GRADE 1 QUESTION

U.S. HISTORY

Who was the very first U.S. Secretary of State?

GRADE 4 QUESTION

GEOGRAPHY

What country has the longest border with the U.S.?

GRADE 2 QUESTION

GRADE 3 QUESTION

ENGLISH

Which of the following is an acronym?
A) scuba
B) biannually
C) lemon-lime

SCIENCE

What geologic era are we in right now?

GRADE 5 QUESTION

QUIZ 5

GRADE 1 QUESTION

ANIMAL SCIENCE

What is the heaviest land animal?

GRADE 5 QUESTION

GEOGRAPHY

What is the capital of Sweden?

GRADE 2 QUESTION

MATH

How many sides does a rhombus have?

GRADE 3 QUESTION

MEASUREMENT

How many decades are in two millennia?

GRADE 4 QUESTION

U.S. HISTORY

Who was the first U.S. President to be impeached?

GEOGRAPHY

What is the only continent that is also a country?

LITERATURE

Who wrote the book *Little House on the Prairie*?

U.S. HISTORY

True or false? Benjamin Franklin served as a senator from Pennsylvania.

ASTRONOMY

True or false? The planet Jupiter has a larger mass than Earth.

ANATOMY

How many incisors are there in a typical adult human mouth?

QUIZ 7

GRADE 3 QUESTION

GEOGRAPHY

What ocean covers the North Pole?

MATH

True or false?
The only factors of 9 are 1 and 9.

GRADE 4 QUESTION

MEASUREMENT

How many months of the year have 31 days?

GRADE 2 QUESTION

P.E.

One might spike the ball in which sport:
A) golf
B) volleyball
C) dodge ball

GRADE 5 QUESTION

BIOLOGY

True or false? All adult kangaroos have pouches.

GRADE 1 QUESTION

ASTRONOMY

What constellation contains the Big Dipper?

GRADE 4 QUESTION

BIOLOGY

True or false? Chickens are cold-blooded animals.

GRADE 2 QUESTION

MATH

What is the only prime number that is a factor of 16?

GRADE 5 QUESTION

MEASUREMENT

What unit of power is abbreviated by the letter W?

GRADE 3 QUESTION

GRADE 1 QUESTION

WORLD HISTORY

True or false? The year 1616 was in the 17th century.

ENGLISH

What is the root word in the word "longest"?

GRADE 1 QUESTION

MUSIC

True or false? By definition, all operas are sung in Italian.

GRADE 3 QUESTION

SCIENCE

Lightning is what type of electricity?
A) current
B) alternating
C) static

GRADE 4 QUESTION

SPELLING

The names of how many months of the year contain the letter R?

GRADE 2 QUESTION

U.S. HISTORY

Who was the first U.S. Secretary of the Treasury?

GRADE 5 QUESTION

GRADE 4 QUESTION

MATH

What is the product of 2/3 and 48?

GRADE 3 QUESTION

ANIMAL SCIENCE

True or false? The orca is a type of dolphin.

U.S. STUDIES

What U.S. state is nicknamed the Lone Star State?

GRADE 1 QUESTION

GRADE 2 QUESTION

GEOGRAPHY

What city is the capital of Japan?

GRADE 5 QUESTION

LITERATURE

What 19th-century British author wrote the novel *Oliver Twist*?

QUIZ 11

MATH

Which number has a 7 in the tens place?
A) 75   B) 57   C) 157

GRADE 1 QUESTION

SCIENCE

GRADE 3 QUESTION

True or false?
Adding salt to water lowers its freezing point.

MEASUREMENT

GRADE 2 QUESTION

How many feet are in a mile?

GEOGRAPHY

Which of the Great Lakes lies farthest east?

GRADE 4 QUESTION

U.S. HISTORY

In what year was Abraham Lincoln first elected U.S. President?

GRADE 5 QUESTION

QUIZ 12

MATH

What is 309 rounded to the nearest hundred?

GRADE 2 QUESTION

U.S. HISTORY

True or false?
Paul Revere participated in the Boston Tea Party.

GRADE 3 QUESTION

GEOGRAPHY

The U.S. state of Hawaii is located in which ocean?

GRADE 1 QUESTION

MEASUREMENT

How many pecks equal one bushel?

GRADE 5 QUESTION

ENGLISH

What is the infinitive of the verb "went"?

GRADE 4 QUESTION

GRADE 1 QUESTION

BIOLOGY

What is the largest animal on earth?

GRADE 2 QUESTION

ASTRONOMY

The planet Earth is located in what galaxy?

MATH

What is the reciprocal of 3/4?

7X/=4?

GRADE 3 QUESTION

U.S. STUDIES

What state's nickname is the Show Me State?

GRADE 4 QUESTION

7X7=4

EARTH SCIENCE

By definition, an anemometer measures the speed of what?

GRADE 5 QUESTION

QUIZ 14

GEOGRAPHY

What is the capital of Thailand?

GRADE 3 QUESTION

ANIMAL SCIENCE

True or false? The koala is a marsupial.

GRADE 1 QUESTION

U.S. HISTORY

What famous American was born on February 22, 1732?

GRADE 2 QUESTION

MEASUREMENT

One gallon equals how many pints?

GRADE 4 QUESTION

ANATOMY

Which are blood vessels in the human body?
A) tibias
B) cilia
C) capillaries

GRADE 5 QUESTION

WHAT STARTS CLOSET TO EARTH?

QUIZ 15

GRADE 1 QUESTION

ASTRONOMY

True or false? The Milky Way galaxy contains more than one billion stars.

MATH

A rectangle has how many sides?

GRADE 3 QUESTION

ANIMAL SCIENCE

What living bird lays the biggest eggs?

GRADE 4 QUESTION

GEOGRAPHY

In terms of area, what is the largest desert in Africa?

GRADE 2 QUESTION

GRADE 5 QUESTION

LITERATURE

Gulliver's Travels was written by what 18th-century author?

MEASUREMENT

How many cups are in five and a half gallons?

GRADE 4 QUESTION

SCIENCE

Which element comprises the majority of Earth's atmosphere?

GRADE 5 QUESTION

ASTRONOMY

What is the only planet in our solar system that man has walked on?

GRADE 1 QUESTION

GEOGRAPHY

After China, what country has the biggest population?

MATH

An isosceles triangle has how many equal sides?

GRADE 3 QUESTION

GRADE 2 QUESTION

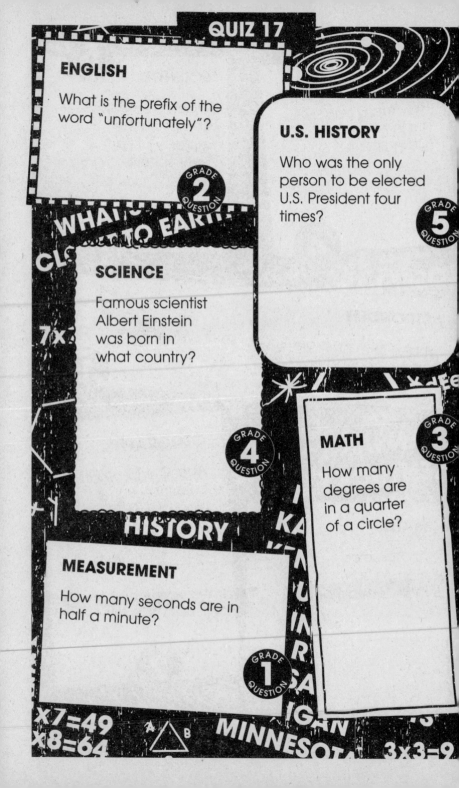

QUIZ 17

ENGLISH

What is the prefix of the word "unfortunately"?

GRADE 2 QUESTION

U.S. HISTORY

Who was the only person to be elected U.S. President four times?

GRADE 5 QUESTION

SCIENCE

Famous scientist Albert Einstein was born in what country?

GRADE 4 QUESTION

MATH

How many degrees are in a quarter of a circle?

GRADE 3 QUESTION

MEASUREMENT

How many seconds are in half a minute?

GRADE 1 QUESTION

ANIMAL SCIENCE

A giant panda's natural habitat is on what continent?

GRADE 3 QUESTION

EARTH SCIENCE

In the Northern Hemisphere, summer ends in which month?

GRADE 1 QUESTION

MATH

If $y = 3x$, and $3x = 12$, then what number does y equal?

GRADE 5 QUESTION

GOVERNMENT

How long is one regular term for a U.S. Senator?

GRADE 4 QUESTION

LITERATURE

The Little Mermaid was written by what 19th-century author?

GRADE 2 QUESTION

GRADE 1 QUESTION

GEOGRAPHY

Which ocean borders the U.S. state of Georgia?

GRADE 2 QUESTION

HEALTH

Typical people have how many baby teeth as kids?
A) 20   B) 24   C) 28

GRADE 5 QUESTION

MATH

Any number to the power of zero
is equal to what value?

U.S. HISTORY

What is the first
name of former U.S.
President Taylor?

GRADE 4 QUESTION

ANIMAL SCIENCE

True or false?
Only male lions
have manes.

GRADE 3 QUESTION

GEOGRAPHY

Mount Kilimanjaro is located on what continent?

GRADE 4 QUESTION

ANIMAL SCIENCE

The female of what animal is called a ewe?

GRADE 2 QUESTION

CULTURAL STUDIES

What modern holiday is also known as All Hallows' Eve?

GRADE 1 QUESTION

ASTRONOMY

The planet Mars has how many moons?

GRADE 5 QUESTION

MEASUREMENT

How many teaspoons are in five tablespoons?

GRADE 3 QUESTION

U.S. HISTORY

Who was the first Chief Justice of the U.S. Supreme Court?

ANATOMY

True or false?
The small intestine is longer than the large intestine.

EARTH SCIENCE

In the Southern Hemisphere, the vernal equinox occurs in which month?

ENGLISH

An example of an oxymoron is:
A) peanut gallery
B) rhyme time
C) living dead

GOVERNMENT

True or false? The President and Vice President live in the White House.

ANIMAL SCIENCE

True or false?
Walruses are native
to the Arctic.

GRADE **1** QUESTION

MATH

True or false?
8/7 is an
improper
fraction.

GRADE **2** QUESTION

SOCIAL STUDIES

The United Nations headquarters are in what city?

GRADE **3** QUESTION

GEOGRAPHY

The names of
how many U.S.
states begin with
the letter O?

GRADE **4** QUESTION

GRAMMAR

GRADE **5** QUESTION

How many nouns
are in: Jake likes
swimming in the
wide lake.

WHAT STARTS
CLOSET TO EARTH?

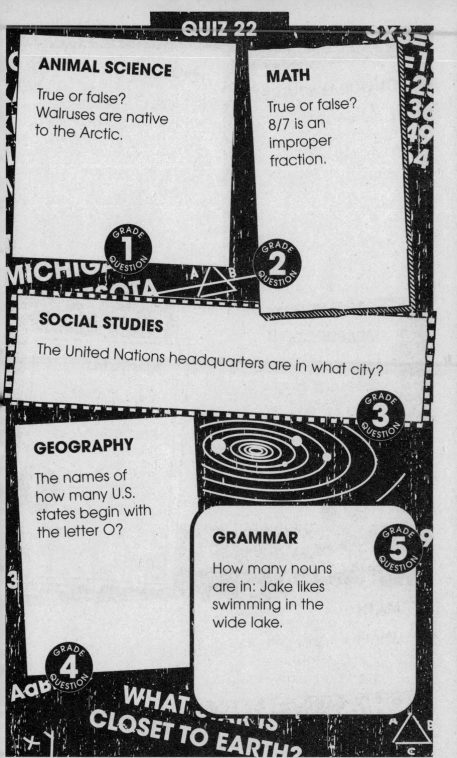

CULTURAL STUDIES

Buddhism is a religion that began in what country?

GRADE 4 QUESTION

GEOGRAPHY

In terms of land area, what is the smallest state?

GRADE 1 QUESTION

MEASUREMENT

How many meters are in a kilometer?

GRADE 2 QUESTION

ANATOMY

True or false? The kidneys are part of the human digestive system.

GRADE 3 QUESTION

MATH

What is the product of 1.1 and 1.1?

GRADE 5 QUESTION

GEOGRAPHY

Russia's longest land border is with what other country?

GRADE 5 QUESTION

MATH

How many sides are there on a trapezoid?

GRADE 4 QUESTION

GRADE 1 QUESTION

SCIENCE

True or false? A spider is an insect.

U.S. STUDIES

What is the capital of Massachusetts?

GRADE 3 QUESTION

GRAMMAR

What is the verb in: It is such a nice day!

GRADE 2 QUESTION

GEOGRAPHY

True or false?
North America is in the Eastern Hemisphere.

GRADE 3 QUESTION

SCIENCE

Which of the following trees is considered a conifer?
A) oak
B) pine
C) maple

GRADE 4 QUESTION

HEALTH

What Scottish scientist discovered penicillin in 1928?

GRADE 5 QUESTION

MATH

True or false?
The sum of two odd numbers will always be an even number.

GRADE 1 QUESTION

ANATOMY

The typical human has how many lungs?

GRADE 2 QUESTION

QUIZ 26

U.S. STUDIES

GRADE 1 QUESTION

In what U.S. state is the Lincoln Home National Historic Site?

EARTH SCIENCE

GRADE 2 QUESTION

True or false? A river's place of origin is its mouth.

GEOGRAPHY

What is the capital of the United Kingdom?

GRADE 3 QUESTION

MEASUREMENT

GRADE 4 QUESTION

How many ounces are in one gallon?

ANATOMY

What organ in the human body produces insulin?

GRADE 5 QUESTION

QUIZ 27

MEASUREMENT
GRADE 5 QUESTION

How many watts are used during one kilowatt-hour?

SPELLING
GRADE 1 QUESTION

The name of which day of the week comes last alphabetically?

MATH
GRADE 3 QUESTION

What is the range of the numbers 8, 3, 7, and 6?

ANIMAL SCIENCE
GRADE 2 QUESTION

Which of the following is a venomous snake?
A) python
B) cobra
C) anaconda

GEOGRAPHY

Ivan the Terrible was a czar of what country?

GRADE 4 QUESTION

QUIZ 28

MATH

What is the product of 4/5 and 125?

GRADE 4 QUESTION

MUSIC

The two most common clefs used in modern music are the treble and what other clef?

GRADE 5 QUESTION

SPELLING

What month comes last alphabetically?

GRADE 2 QUESTION

ANIMAL SCIENCE

True or false? The Alaskan malamute is a species of fish.

GRADE 3 QUESTION

ENGLISH

How many apostrophes are missing from:
Nathans dog licked its paw.

GRADE 1 QUESTION

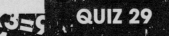

GRADE 5 QUESTION

U.S. HISTORY

Who was the only U.S. President who never married?

GEOGRAPHY

How many U.S. states border the Pacific Ocean?

GRADE 2 QUESTION

MATH

What number is 11 more than 55 and 9 less than 75?

SCIENCE

What scientist developed the equation $E = mc^2$?

GRADE 1 QUESTION

GRADE 4 QUESTION

GRADE 3 QUESTION

ENGLISH

What is the singular form of the word lice?

U.S. HISTORY

In 1782, what became the official bird of the United States?

ANIMAL SCIENCE

How many arms does a typical octopus have?

MEASUREMENT

If Cody's baby sister weighs 8 pounds, how many ounces does she weigh?

GEOGRAPHY

Bern is the capital of what European country?

MUSIC

What composer wrote the *1812 Overture* in 1882?

QUIZ 31

WORLD HISTORY

True or false? Vikings, also known as Norsemen, originated in Scandinavia.

GRADE 3 QUESTION

MEASUREMENT

How many square feet are in a three-yard-square area?

GRADE 5 QUESTION

MATH

The supplementary angle of a 60-degree angle has how many degrees?

GRADE 4 QUESTION

GEOGRAPHY

The U.S. state of Indiana borders which Great Lake?

GRADE 1 QUESTION

GRADE 2 QUESTION

EARTH SCIENCE

True or false? Plants are not part of the food chain.

7x7=49   AaBbCcDdE

HEALTH

How many canine teeth are in a typical adult human mouth?

GRADE **4** QUESTION

ANIMAL SCIENCE

True or false? The wolverine is a member of the canine family.

GRADE **2** QUESTION

AT STAR IS
LOSET TO EA

x y   6yz

GRADE **5** QUESTION

EARTH SCIENCE

Coal and diamonds are made of what element?

KANSAS   HIST
KENTUCKY   E

MEASUREMENT

Of the current U.S. coins, which is smallest in size?

GRADE **1** QUESTION

P.E.

To the nearest mile, how long is a standard Olympic marathon?

GRADE **3** QUESTION

A B

MATH

What whole number is the closest to the square root of 50?

GRADE 4 QUESTION

GEOGRAPHY

Yosemite National Park is located in what U.S. state?

GRADE 2 QUESTION

BIOLOGY

A typical amoeba has how many cells?

GRADE 3 QUESTION

ASTRONOMY

What was the name of the first American woman to travel into outer space?

GRADE 5 QUESTION

EARTH SCIENCE

True or false? Lightning is a form of precipitation.

GRADE 1 QUESTION

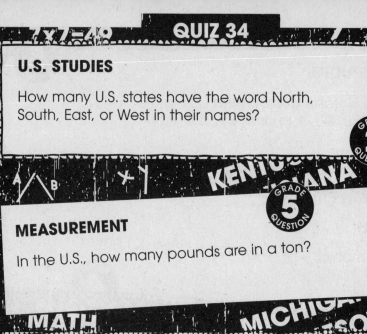

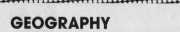

U.S. STUDIES

How many U.S. states have the word North, South, East, or West in their names?

GRADE 2 QUESTION

MEASUREMENT

In the U.S., how many pounds are in a ton?

GRADE 5 QUESTION

GEOGRAPHY

What is the capital of Brazil?

GRADE 4 QUESTION

MATH

At 48 cents a pound, how much does 5/8 of a pound of peanuts cost?

GRADE 3 QUESTION

LITERATURE

In folklore, what is the name of Paul Bunyan's blue ox?

GRADE 1 QUESTION

U.S. STUDIES

GRADE 5 QUESTION

Two U.S. states were formed during the Civil War: Nevada and which other?

MATH

How many factors does the number 121 have?

GRADE 4 QUESTION

EARTH SCIENCE

GRADE 3 QUESTION

True or false? Cocoa beans, from which chocolate is made, originated in Asia.

GEOGRAPHY

U.S. Studies
In terms of land area, what is the second-biggest U.S. state?

GRADE 1 QUESTION

MUSIC

Timpani are members of what musical family?

GRADE 2 QUESTION

MATH

What is the absolute value of 9?

GRADE 5 QUESTION

MUSIC

True or false?
A beat with no sound is called a rest.

GRADE 1 QUESTION

GEOGRAPHY

Sweden's longest land border is with what other country?

GRADE 4 QUESTION

SCIENCE

What state of matter is ice?
A) solid
B) gas
C) liquid

GRADE 2 QUESTION

ART

On the color wheel, what color is complementary to orange?

GRADE 3 QUESTION

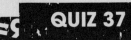

GRADE 1 QUESTION

MATH

True or false? The sum of the digits in the number 768 is equal to 22.

CHEMISTRY

What is the lightest noble gas?

GRADE 5 QUESTION

ENGLISH

"Wept" is the past tense form of what verb?

GRADE 4 QUESTION

GEOGRAPHY

The Allegheny and Monongahela rivers meet and form the Ohio River in what U.S. city?

GRADE 3 QUESTION

GRADE 2 QUESTION

SPELLING

The plural form of the word "quiz" has how many letters?

QUIZ 38

BIOLOGY

What gas do humans exhale that plants need to live?

GRADE 1 QUESTION

U.S. STUDIES

Which U.S. President is featured on the face of the nickel?

GRADE 2 QUESTION

ANIMAL SCIENCE

In terms of average size, what is the largest species of penguin?

GRADE 3 QUESTION

MATH

What is the least common multiple of 6 and 10?

GRADE 4 QUESTION

WORLD HISTORY

Who became the first chairman of the People's Republic of China in 1949?

GRADE 5 QUESTION

QUIZ 39

SCIENCE

How many horns did *Triceratops* have on its head?

GRADE 1 QUESTION

GEOGRAPHY

Which continent is the least populated?

GRADE 2 QUESTION

CULTURAL STUDIES

In Greek mythology, who was the father of Apollo?

GRADE 4 QUESTION

MATH

What is the area of a square that has a 24cm perimeter?

GRADE 5 QUESTION

GRADE 3 QUESTION

U.S. HISTORY

In what U.S. state was the Civil War Battle of Gettysburg fought?

BIOLOGY

An animal without a backbone is an:
A) invertebrate
B) anthropoid
C) amphibian

GRADE QUESTION 3

U.S. HISTORY

What U.S. President only served one month in office?

GRADE QUESTION 5

LITERATURE

In Homer's *Odyssey*, the monster Cyclops has how many eyes?

GRADE QUESTION 4

CULTURAL STUDIES

The holiday Cinco de Mayo originated in what country?

GRADE QUESTION 2

ASTRONOMY

How many confirmed planets (as of October 2016) are in our solar system?

GRADE QUESTION 1

ANIMAL SCIENCE

True or false?
Komodo dragons
are extinct.

GRADE 1 QUESTION

U.S. STUDIES

The U.S. Naval
Academy is located
in what city?

GRADE 4 QUESTION

MATH

What is the sum of
the degrees of the
interior angles of an
octagon?

GRADE 5 QUESTION

GEOGRAPHY

France borders
which ocean?

GRADE 2 QUESTION

ENGLISH

What part of speech is the
first word in: How do you do?

GRADE 3 QUESTION

QUIZ 42

GEOGRAPHY

The headwaters of the Mississippi River are in what U.S. state?

MATH

If $15/35 = n/7$, then n must be equal to what number?

ANIMAL SCIENCE

Which is not a fish:
A) manta ray   B) porpoise   C) sea horse

GRAMMAR

How many nouns are in this question?

U.S. HISTORY

True or false? Betsy Ross was a U.S. First Lady.

GEOGRAPHY

GRADE 5 QUESTION

Timbuktu is a city in what African country?

ANIMAL SCIENCE

GRADE 1 QUESTION

True or false? A camel's hump is primarily used to hold water.

ASTRONOMY

GRADE 3 QUESTION

True or false? The sun is the only star in our solar system.

ENGLISH

GRADE 2 QUESTION

True or false? The word "true" is an antonym of the word "false."

MATH

GRADE 4 QUESTION

What is the greatest common factor of 12 and 36?

QUIZ 44

MATH

GRADE QUESTION 4

What is the numeric value of the Roman numeral L?

GEOGRAPHY

GRADE QUESTION 2

Active volcano Mount St. Helens is in what U.S. state?

ANIMAL SCIENCE

GRADE QUESTION 5

The octopus belongs to what class of animals?

GRAMMAR

GRADE QUESTION 1

What is the adjective in: Olivia has ten fingers on which to count numbers.

PHYSICS

GRADE QUESTION 3

A lever is a simple machine that pivots on a point called a: A) fulcrum   B) levee   C) pulley

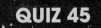

GRADE 4 QUESTION

SPELLING

Which of the following words is spelled incorrectly?
A) privilege   B) villege   C) appendage

GEOGRAPHY

What is the world's longest river?

GRADE 3 QUESTION

ANIMAL SCIENCE

True or false? Some species of sea turtles live in freshwater lakes.

GRADE 1 QUESTION

MATH

How many faces are there on a cube?

GRADE 2 QUESTION

GRADE 5 QUESTION

WORLD HISTORY

Who is the longest-reigning British monarch?

GRAMMAR

The word "you" is what type of pronoun?
A) first person
B) second person
C) third person

GRADE 3 QUESTION

U.S. HISTORY

What was the first name of U.S. President Hayes, elected into office in 1876?

GRADE 4 QUESTION

GEOGRAPHY

True or false? There are no glaciers in Africa.

GRADE 2 QUESTION

ANIMAL SCIENCE

True or false? Roadrunners are birds.

GRADE 1 QUESTION

MATH

What's the volume (in cm^3) of a cube with surface area of 96 cm^2 ?

GRADE 5 QUESTION

WHAT CLOSET TO EARTH?

QUIZ 47

GRAMMAR

Which of the following is NOT an article?
A) an
B) the
C) to

GRADE 2 QUESTION

GEOGRAPHY

Copenhagen is the capital of what European country?

GRADE 4 QUESTION

MATH

What is the sum of all the even numbers between 1 and 9?

GRADE 1 QUESTION

BIOLOGY

What is NOT part of an animal cell?
A) ribosome
B) chloroplast
C) cytoplasm

GRADE 5 QUESTION

EARTH SCIENCE

GRADE 3 QUESTION

In order for iron to rust, it needs to be exposed to both water and what gaseous element?

AaBbC

ENGLISH

"Won't" is a contraction of what two words?

GRADE 1 QUESTION

GEOGRAPHY

GRADE 2 QUESTION

Which of the following states extends the farthest north?
A) Wyoming
B) Idaho
C) Utah

U.S. HISTORY

GRADE 4 QUESTION

Who was President of the U.S. in 1800?

KANSAS HIST
KENTUCKY E

MEASUREMENT

How many cups are in 5 U.S. liquid quarts?

ANIMAL SCIENCE

True or false? All arthropods are invertebrates

GRADE 5 QUESTION

GRADE 3 QUESTION

ANIMAL SCIENCE

True or false?
A chimpanzee has no tail.

GRADE 1 QUESTION

PHYSICS

Radio frequency AM:
the A stands for
amplitude; the M
stands for what?

GRADE 5 QUESTION

GEOGRAPHY

Dormant volcano
Mount Hood is
located in what
U.S. state?

GRADE 4 QUESTION

ENGLISH

Which is
punctuated
correctly:
A) 'Tis I!
B) T'is I!
C) 'Tis I!

GRADE 3 QUESTION

U.S. HISTORY

The thirteen American Colonies
gained independence from
what country?

GRADE 2 QUESTION

PHYSICS

GRADE 2 QUESTION

Which of these colors absorbs the least amount of light?
A) red   B) yellow   C) white

ANIMAL SCIENCE

GRADE 1 QUESTION

True or false? The dodo bird is extinct.

GOVERNMENT

GRADE 3 QUESTION

Which amendment to the U.S. Constitution
gives us freedom of religion?

GEOGRAPHY

GRADE 4 QUESTION

What African country is home
to the city of Casablanca?

ENGLISH

GRADE 5 QUESTION

Fred swims like a fish. Is this a simile or metaphor?

QUIZ 51

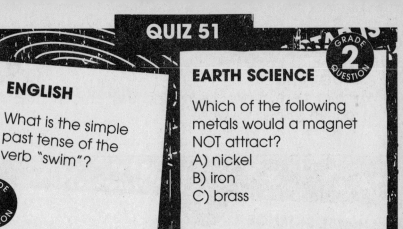

ENGLISH

GRADE 1 QUESTION

What is the simple past tense of the verb "swim"?

EARTH SCIENCE

GRADE 2 QUESTION

Which of the following metals would a magnet NOT attract?
A) nickel
B) iron
C) brass

WORLD HISTORY

GRADE 5 QUESTION

What American civil rights leader won the Nobel Peace Prize in 1964?

GOVERNMENT

GRADE 4 QUESTION

What is the maximum number of consecutive years a person can serve as U.S. President?

MATH

GRADE 3 QUESTION

What is 1 and 6/7 expressed as an improper fraction?
A) 13/7   B) 7/6   C) 1/7

GEOGRAPHY

The mouth of the Indus river is in what country?

GRADE 5 QUESTION

ANIMAL SCIENCE

True or false?
The Japanese giant salamander is warm-blooded.

GRADE 3 QUESTION

ENGLISH

What is the last consonant in the modern English alphabet?

GRADE 1 QUESTION

ASTRONOMY

What galaxy is closest in distance to the Milky Way?

GRADE 4 QUESTION

MATH

True or false?
When you divide 30 by 4, there is no remainder.

GRADE 2 QUESTION

BIOLOGY

True or false?
The cicada is a
type of insect.

GRADE 1 QUESTION

U.S. HISTORY

Who was elected
president of the
Confederate States
during the American
Civil War?

GRADE 5 QUESTION

MATH

Sierra had 30
cookies for her
party. All nine kids
at the party ate
two cookies each.
How many were
left over?

GRADE 2 QUESTION

ART

In weaving,
the vertical
and horizontal
threads are
called the
warp and the:
A) wane
B) weft
C) loop

GRADE 4 QUESTION

EARTH SCIENCE

Acorns come from what
species of tree?

GRADE 3 QUESTION

ASTRONOMY

GRADE QUESTION **1**

What is the name of the star closest to Earth?

GRADE QUESTION **5**

ART

Renaissance artist Michelangelo, painter of the ceiling of the Sistine Chapel, was born in what century?

ENGLISH

GRADE QUESTION **2**

True or false?
The suffix goes at the beginning of a word.

U.S. HISTORY

GRADE QUESTION **3**

What was President Lincoln's wife's first name?
A) Mary   B) Elizabeth   C) Anne

GEOGRAPHY

GRADE QUESTION **4**

How many U.S. states are located north of the Tropic of Cancer?

ASTRONOMY

Our moon is in orbit around
A) the sun   B) the night sky   C) Earth

NUTRITION

Fuji and Gala are both varieties of what fruit?

GEOGRAPHY

Which of the seven continents
has the largest population?

PHYSICS

32° Fahrenheit is
equal to what
degree Celsius?

MATH

What is the sum
of 11.5 and
negative 14?

MATH

What is the highest two-digit even number?

GRADE 2 QUESTION

ANIMAL SCIENCE

True or false?
All ladybugs are female.

GRADE 1 QUESTION

ENGLISH

Which sentence contains a transitive verb?
A) The class ended early.
B) The teacher found his notes.
C) The students excelled.

GRADE 4 QUESTION

ANATOMY

What organ in the human body produces and secretes bile?

GRADE 5 QUESTION

GOVERNMENT

The U.S. Declaration of Independence was written and signed in what year?

GRADE 3 QUESTION

GRADE 2 QUESTION

U.S. HISTORY

In 1814, what U.S. First Lady saved the Declaration of Independence from a fire at the White House?

GRADE 4 QUESTION

WORLD CULTURES

Built in the 1600s, the Taj Mahal stands in the city of Agra in what country?

GRADE 1 QUESTION

ANATOMY

What joint in the human body connects the foot to the leg?

GRADE 5 QUESTION

ASTRONOMY

What country was the first to put a human in space?

GRADE 3 QUESTION

ENGLISH

How many syllables are traditionally in the second line of a haiku? A) 3 B) 5 C) 7

PHYSICS

Which of the following is measured in units known as nektons?
A) force
B) mass
C) heat

ANATOMY

True or false?
The epidermis is directly underneath the dermis.

U.S. STUDIES

Which U.S. President is featured on the face of the dime?

ANIMAL SCIENCE

True or false?
A tick is an arachnid.

ENGLISH

True or false?
The plural of "roof" is "rooves."

QUIZ 59

WORLD HISTORY

In the 16th century, what explorer began and led the first known sea voyage that would circle the globe?

GRADE 4 QUESTION

ENGLISH

Which is a synonym for "happy"?
A) hippy
B) sad
C) glad

GRADE 2 QUESTION

GRADE 1 QUESTION

EARTH SCIENCE

What species of sequoia is the tallest tree in the world?

MATH

28 + 14 equals 7 x what?

GRADE 3 QUESTION

GRADE 5 QUESTION

ART

What Norwegian artist painted *The Scream*?

WORLD CULTURES

Which is NOT an official language of Switzerland?
A) German
B) Italian
C) Swedish

GRADE 3 QUESTION

MATH

If the sum of negative 4 and positive 6 is y, then how much is y times 3?

GRADE 4 QUESTION

ENGLISH

GRADE 1 QUESTION

True or false? A complete simple sentence must always contain at least one verb.

KANSAS
KENTUCKY

HIST

ASTRONOMY

In the sun's core, hydrogen atoms fuse together to form what other element?

GRADE 5 QUESTION

GRADE 2 QUESTION

GOVERNMENT

A U.S. Supreme Court Justice is appointed to serve for how long?
A) 4 years
B) 20 years
C) lifetime appointment

U.S. STUDIES

True or false? If you are born in the U.S. (to non-diplomats), then you are an American citizen.

GRADE 2 QUESTION

ANIMAL SCIENCE

True or false? Horses can sleep standing up.

GRADE 1 QUESTION

GOVERNMENT

Can a person born in Germany to an American-citizen mother later qualify to become President of the U.S.?

GRADE 5 QUESTION

ASTRONOMY

More than 99% of the mass of our solar system is contained within what heavenly body?

GRADE 4 QUESTION

GRADE 3 QUESTION

MATH

If Olivia ran 36 miles in 4 hours, on average how many miles did she run per hour?

$x7 = 49$
$x8 = 64$

$3 \times 3 = 9$

WHAT CL... TO EAR...

HISTORY

MINNESOTA

SCIENCE

GRADE 5 QUESTION

What element is combined with carbon to make basic steel?

U.S. STUDIES

GRADE 3 QUESTION

Who wrote the lyrics to "The Star-Spangled Banner"?

MATH

GRADE 4 QUESTION

If an isosceles triangle has side lengths of 5 and 8, what could be the length of the third side?
A) 3   B) 5   C) 13

ENGLISH

GRADE 1 QUESTION

Including Y, how many consonants are in the modern English alphabet?

MEASUREMENT

GRADE 2 QUESTION

How many days are in a leap year?

GRADE 4 QUESTION

ASTRONOMY

What is the brightest star we can see in the night sky?

BIOLOGY

GRADE 2 QUESTION

How many legs does a butterfly have?

GRADE 5 QUESTION

GEOGRAPHY

What U.S. state is home to Acadia National Park?

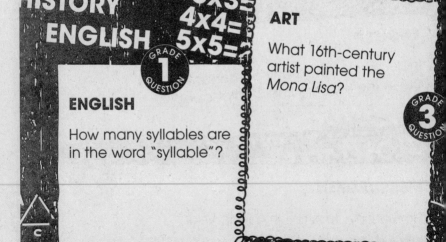

ART

What 16th-century artist painted the *Mona Lisa*?

GRADE 3 QUESTION

GRADE 1 QUESTION

ENGLISH

How many syllables are in the word "syllable"?

QUIZ 64

ENGLISH

True or false?
A sentence
cannot contain
both a past tense
and a future
tense verb.

GRADE 2 QUESTION

GEOGRAPHY

Budapest is the
capital of what
European country?

GRADE 3 QUESTION

GRADE 4 QUESTION

MUSIC

In a C major scale,
what note is two
whole steps higher in
pitch than the note F?

GRADE 5 QUESTION

MATH

How many
common
factors do 28
and 32 have?

SCIENCE

GRADE 1 QUESTION

What gemstone is formed inside
mollusks such as oysters?

QUIZ 65

U.S. HISTORY

GRADE 1 QUESTION

The Liberty Bell originally hung in Independence Hall in what U.S. city?

MEASUREMENT

GRADE 3 QUESTION

How many milliliters are there in 0.45 liters?

ENGLISH

GRADE 2 QUESTION

Which of these is a synonym of the word "rural"?
A) urban
B) countryside
C) metropolitan

SCIENCE

GRADE 4 QUESTION

What is the process by which plants make their own food?
A) photosynthesis
B) oxidation
C) mitosis

GEOGRAPHY

GRADE 5 QUESTION

The Bay of Bengal is part of what Ocean?

GEOGRAPHY

Puget Sound is a body of water bordered by what U.S. state?

GRADE 4 QUESTION

ANIMAL SCIENCE

True or false? Giant pandas hibernate.

GRADE 2 QUESTION

VOCABULARY

GRADE 1 QUESTION

By definition, how many wheels does a unicycle have?

PHYSICS

Which refers to the lowest point of a sound wave?
A) crest
B) trough
C) period

GRADE 3 QUESTION

U.S. HISTORY

GRADE 5 QUESTION

U.S. President John Adams was a member of what political party at the time of his election?

WHAT STAR IS CLOSET TO EARTH?

GEOGRAPHY

GRADE 4 QUESTION

The Rhine River is located on what continent?

ENGLISH

GRADE 2 QUESTION

True or false? The word "want" is a contraction.

U.S. HISTORY

GRADE 3 QUESTION

What American inventor patented the first working phonograph in the 1870s?

MATH

GRADE 1 QUESTION

What is the sum of the whole numbers 1 through 6, including 1 and 6?

SCIENCE

GRADE 5 QUESTION

Three elements are found in all carbohydrates: carbon, hydrogen, and what other?

SCIENCE

GRADE 2 QUESTION

True or false?
The positively
charged ends of
two magnets will
attract each other.

GEOGRAPHY

GRADE 5 QUESTION

What is the fourth
most populous
country, after China,
India, and the U.S.?

MATH

GRADE 4 QUESTION

What is the simplest form of the fraction 18/81?

ENGLISH

GRADE 3 QUESTION

Which is a
homophone of
the word "night"?
A) knight
B) day
C) evening

MUSIC

GRADE 1 QUESTION

Cymbals belong to
what musical family?

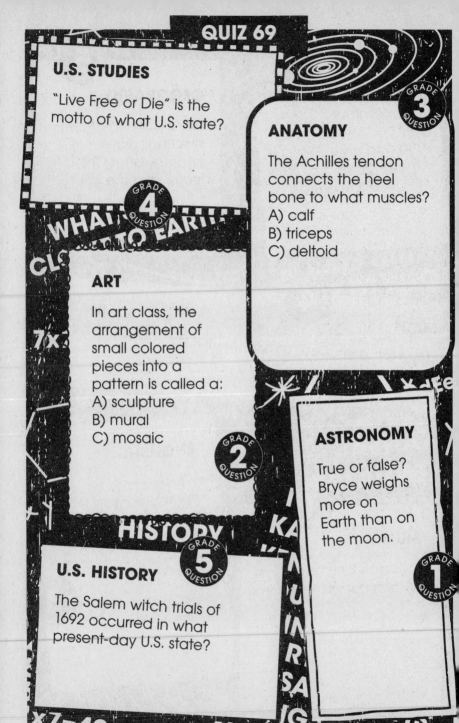

U.S. STUDIES

"Live Free or Die" is the motto of what U.S. state?

GRADE 4 QUESTION

ANATOMY

The Achilles tendon connects the heel bone to what muscles?
A) calf
B) triceps
C) deltoid

GRADE 3 QUESTION

ART

In art class, the arrangement of small colored pieces into a pattern is called a:
A) sculpture
B) mural
C) mosaic

GRADE 2 QUESTION

ASTRONOMY

True or false? Bryce weighs more on Earth than on the moon.

GRADE 1 QUESTION

U.S. HISTORY

The Salem witch trials of 1692 occurred in what present-day U.S. state?

GRADE 5 QUESTION

GEOGRAPHY

GRADE 2 QUESTION

Cuba is geographically closest to what U.S. state?

ENGLISH

GRADE 1 QUESTION

True or false? The plural form of the word "fox" is "foxen."

MATH

True or false? The reciprocal of 5/6 is a whole number.

GRADE 3 QUESTION

U.S. HISTORY

GRADE 5 QUESTION

Which commanding British general surrendered to American troops at the Battle of Yorktown in 1781?

HEALTH

GRADE 4 QUESTION

What is the most abundant metallic element in the human body?

GRADE 3 QUESTION

HEALTH

True or false? Someone who is nearsighted has trouble seeing things far away.

GRADE 1 QUESTION

SCIENCE

True or false?
Pollen is part of a plant's reproductive system.

GRADE 2 QUESTION

GEOGRAPHY

Omaha is the most populous city in what U.S. state?

GRADE 4 QUESTION

U.S. HISTORY

On Dec. 1, 1955, Rosa Parks famously refused to give up her seat on a bus in what U.S. city?

ENGLISH

From the Greek meaning "outermost line of verse," what type of poem has letters at the beginning of each line that spell out a message?

GRADE 5 QUESTION

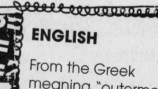

QUIZ 72

ANIMAL SCIENCE

True or false?
A ram is a
male sheep.

GRADE 1 QUESTION

CULTURAL STUDIES

What is the official
language of Brazil?

GRADE 3 QUESTION

MATH

How many degrees are
there in each angle of
an equilateral triangle?

GRADE 4 QUESTION

U.S. HISTORY

What Jamestown
colony settler
married
Pocahontas
in 1614?

GRADE 5 QUESTION

GEOGRAPHY

What U.S. state borders both Kansas and Utah?

GRADE 2 QUESTION

U.S. HISTORY

GRADE 1 QUESTION

What was the first name of the first U.S. First Lady?

U.S. STUDIES

GRADE 3 QUESTION

What is the capital of Arkansas?

ANIMAL SCIENCE

True or false? All roosters are male.

GRADE 2 QUESTION

CULTURAL STUDIES

GRADE 4 QUESTION

What day of the week is named after the Norse god of thunder?

GEOGRAPHY

GRADE 5 QUESTION

What is the largest of the Mariana Islands in the western Pacific Ocean?

ASTRONOMY

NASA space shuttles were launched from Cape Canaveral in what U.S. state?

GRADE QUESTION 3

NUTRITION

The food known as pork comes from what animal?

GRADE QUESTION 1

GOVERNMENT

GRADE QUESTION 2

What three words begin the Preamble to the U.S. Constitution?

MEASUREMENT

In U.S. measurement, how many feet are in one furlong?

GEOGRAPHY

GRADE QUESTION 4

Canberra is the capital of what country?

GRADE QUESTION 5

WHAT STAR IS CLOSET TO EARTH?

DID YOU MAKE THE GRADE?

To find out, all you need to do is add up your score.

Each quiz has a question for each Grade level: 1, 2, 3, 4, 5

For each correct answer, you score:
Grade 1, 1 point
Grade 2, 2 points
Grade 3, 3 points
Grade 4, 4 points
Grade 5, 5 points

A perfect score for each quiz is 15 points.

15, 14, or 13 points—You're an A+ student!
12, 11, 10 points—Not bad! Congrats!
9, 8, 7, 6 points—That's okay. Just keep pluggin'!
5 and below—Next quiz will be better!

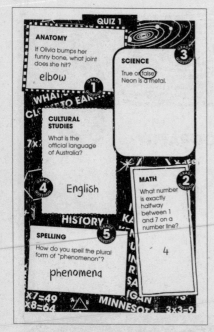

QUIZ 1

ANATOMY
If Olivia bumps her funny bone, what joint does she hit?
elbow

SCIENCE *(Grade 3)*
True or false?
Neon is a metal.

CULTURAL STUDIES *(Grade 4)*
What is the official language of Australia?
English

MATH *(Grade 2)*
What number is exactly halfway between 1 and 7 on a number line?
4

SPELLING *(Grade 5)*
How do you spell the plural form of "phenomenon"?
phenomena

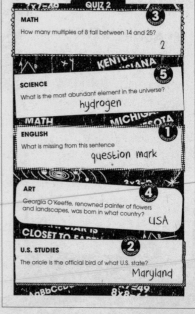

QUIZ 2

MATH *(Grade 3)*
How many multiples of 8 fall between 14 and 25?
2

SCIENCE *(Grade 5)*
What is the most abundant element in the universe?
hydrogen

ENGLISH *(Grade 1)*
What is missing from this sentence
question mark

ART *(Grade 4)*
Georgia O'Keeffe, renowned painter of flowers and landscapes, was born in what country?
USA

U.S. STUDIES *(Grade 2)*
The oriole is the official bird of what U.S. state?
Maryland

Your Score: **Your Score:**

ANSWERS

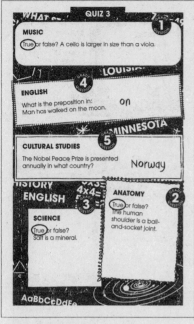

QUIZ 3

MUSIC ①
(True) or false? A cello is larger in size than a viola.

ENGLISH ④
What is the preposition in:
Man has walked on the moon.
on

CULTURAL STUDIES ⑤
The Nobel Peace Prize is presented
annually in what country?
Norway

ENGLISH ③

ANATOMY ②
(True) or false?
The human
shoulder is a ball-
and-socket joint.

SCIENCE
(True) or false?
Salt is a mineral.

Your Score:

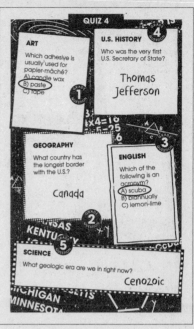

QUIZ 4

ART ①
Which adhesive is
usually used for
papier-mâché?
A) candle wax
B) paste
C) tape

U.S. HISTORY ④
Who was the very first
U.S. Secretary of State?
Thomas
Jefferson

GEOGRAPHY
What country has
the longest border
with the U.S.?
Canada

ENGLISH ③
Which of the
following is an
acronym?
A) scuba
B) biannually
C) lemon-lime

SCIENCE ⑤ ②
What geologic era are we in right now?
Cenozoic

Your Score:

QUIZ 5

ANIMAL SCIENCE ①
What is the heaviest land animal?
elephant

GEOGRAPHY ⑤
What is the capital of Sweden?
Stockholm

MATH ②
How many sides
does a rhombus
have?
4

MEASUREMENT ③
How many decades are in
two millennia?
200

U.S. HISTORY ④
Who was the first U.S. President to be impeached?
Andrew Johnson

Your Score:

QUIZ 6

GEOGRAPHY
What is the only
continent that is also
a country?
Australia

LITERATURE ④
Who wrote the
book *Little House
on the Prairie*?
Laura
Ingalls
Wilder

U.S. HISTORY ①
True or (false)? Benjamin Franklin served as a senator
from Pennsylvania.

ASTRONOMY ③
(True) or false?
The planet Jupiter
has a larger mass
than Earth.

ANATOMY ⑤
How many incisors are
there in a typical adult
human mouth?
8

②

Your Score:

ANSWERS

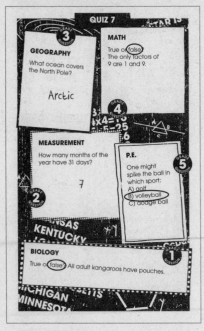

QUIZ 7

GEOGRAPHY ③
What ocean covers the North Pole?

Arctic

MATH
True or ~~false~~
The only factors of 9 are 1 and 9.

MEASUREMENT
How many months of the year have 31 days?

7 ②

P.E. ⑤
One might spike the ball in which sport:
A) golf
B) volleyball
C) dodge ball

BIOLOGY ①
True or ~~false~~ All adult kangaroos have pouches.

Your Score:

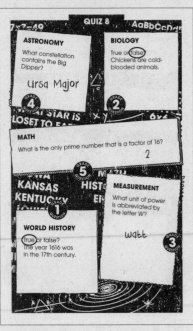

QUIZ 8

ASTRONOMY
What constellation contains the Big Dipper?

Ursa Major ④

BIOLOGY
True or ~~false~~
Chickens are cold-blooded animals. ②

MATH
What is the only prime number that is a factor of 16?

2

WORLD HISTORY ⑤①
~~True~~ or false?
The year 1616 was in the 17th century.

MEASUREMENT
What unit of power is abbreviated by the letter W?

watt ③

Your Score:

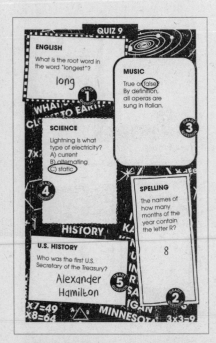

QUIZ 9

ENGLISH
What is the root word in the word "longest"?

long ①

MUSIC
True or ~~false~~
By definition, all operas are sung in Italian. ③

SCIENCE
Lightning is what type of electricity?
A) current
B) alternating
C) static ④

SPELLING
The names of how many months of the year contain the letter R?

8

U.S. HISTORY
Who was the first U.S. Secretary of the Treasury?

Alexander Hamilton ⑤ ②

Your Score:

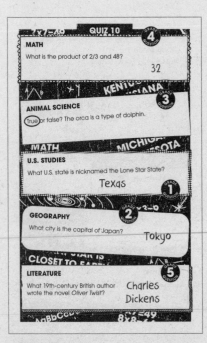

QUIZ 10

MATH ④
What is the product of 2/3 and 48?

32

ANIMAL SCIENCE ③
~~True~~ or false? The orca is a type of dolphin.

U.S. STUDIES
What U.S. state is nicknamed the Lone Star State?

Texas ①

GEOGRAPHY ②
What city is the capital of Japan?

Tokyo

LITERATURE ⑤
What 19th-century British author wrote the novel *Oliver Twist*?

Charles Dickens

Your Score:

ANSWERS

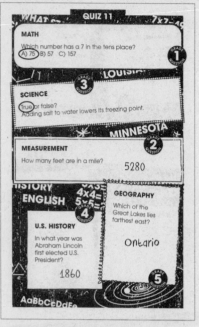

QUIZ 11

MATH
Which number has a 7 in the tens place?
A) 75   B) 57   C) 157

SCIENCE
True or false?
Adding salt to water lowers its freezing point.

MEASUREMENT
How many feet are in a mile?
5280

U.S. HISTORY
In what year was Abraham Lincoln first elected U.S. President?
1860

GEOGRAPHY
Which of the Great Lakes lies farthest east?
Ontario

Your Score:

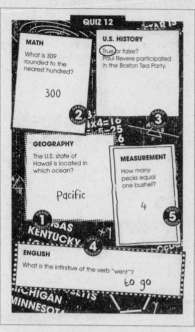

QUIZ 12

MATH
What is 309 rounded to the nearest hundred?
300

U.S. HISTORY
True or false?
Paul Revere participated in the Boston Tea Party.

GEOGRAPHY
The U.S. state of Hawaii is located in which ocean?
Pacific

MEASUREMENT
How many pecks equal one bushel?
4

ENGLISH
What is the infinitive of the verb "went"?
to go

Your Score:

QUIZ 13

BIOLOGY
What is the largest animal on earth?
blue whale

ASTRONOMY
The planet Earth is located in what galaxy?
Milky Way

MATH
What is the reciprocal of 3/4?
1 1/3

U.S. STUDIES
What state's nickname is the Show Me State?
Missouri

EARTH SCIENCE
By definition, an anemometer measures the speed of what?
wind speed

Your Score:

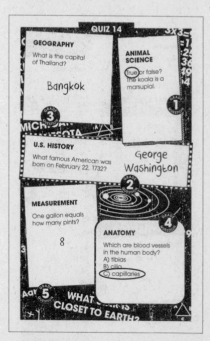

QUIZ 14

GEOGRAPHY
What is the capital of Thailand?
Bangkok

ANIMAL SCIENCE
True or false?
The koala is a marsupial.

U.S. HISTORY
What famous American was born on February 22, 1732?
George Washington

MEASUREMENT
One gallon equals how many pints?
8

ANATOMY
Which are blood vessels in the human body?
A) tibias
B) cilia
C) capillaries

Your Score:

ANSWERS

QUIZ 15

ASTRONOMY
True or false? The Milky Way galaxy contains more than one billion stars.

MATH
A rectangle has how many sides?

4

ANIMAL SCIENCE
What living bird lays the biggest eggs?

ostrich

GEOGRAPHY
In terms of area, what is the largest desert in Africa?

Sahara

LITERATURE
Gulliver's Travels was written by what 18th-century author?

Jonathan Swift

Your Score:

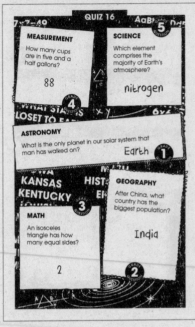

QUIZ 16

MEASUREMENT
How many cups are in five and a half gallons?

88

SCIENCE
Which element comprises the majority of Earth's atmosphere?

nitrogen

ASTRONOMY
What is the only planet in our solar system that man has walked on?

Earth

GEOGRAPHY
After China, what country has the biggest population?

India

MATH
An isosceles triangle has how many equal sides?

2

Your Score:

QUIZ 17

ENGLISH
What is the prefix of the word "unfortunately"?

un-

U.S. HISTORY
Who was the only person to be elected U.S. President four times?

Franklin Roosevelt

SCIENCE
Famous scientist Albert Einstein was born in what country?

Germany

MATH
How many degrees are in a quarter of a circle?

90

MEASUREMENT
How many seconds are in half a minute?

30

Your Score:

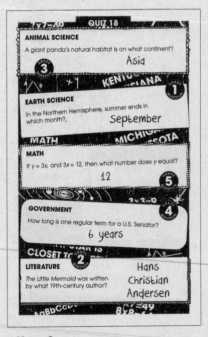

QUIZ 18

ANIMAL SCIENCE
A giant panda's natural habitat is on what continent?

Asia

EARTH SCIENCE
In the Northern Hemisphere, summer ends in which month?,

September

MATH
If $y = 3x$, and $3x = 12$, then what number does y equal?

12

GOVERNMENT
How long is one regular term for a U.S. Senator?

6 years

LITERATURE
The Little Mermaid was written by what 19th-century author?

Hans Christian Andersen

Your Score:

ANSWERS

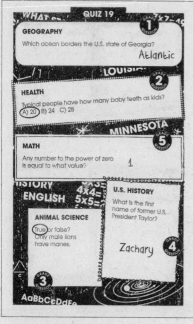

QUIZ 19

GEOGRAPHY (1)
Which ocean borders the U.S. state of Georgia?
Atlantic

HEALTH (2)
Typical people have how many baby teeth as kids?
A) 20 B) 24 C) 28

MATH (5)
Any number to the power of zero is equal to what value?
1

U.S. HISTORY (4)
What is the first name of former U.S. President Taylor?
Zachary

ANIMAL SCIENCE (3)
True or false?
Only male lions have manes.

Your Score:

QUIZ 20

GEOGRAPHY (4)
Mount Kilimanjaro is located on what continent?
Africa

ANIMAL SCIENCE (1)
The female of what animal is called a ewe?
sheep

CULTURAL STUDIES (1)
What modern holiday is also known as All Hallows' Eve?
Halloween

ASTRONOMY (5)
The planet Mars has how many moons?
2

MEASUREMENT (3)
How many teaspoons are in five tablespoons?
15

Your Score:

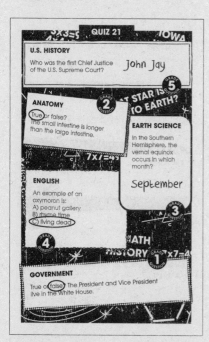

QUIZ 21

U.S. HISTORY (1)
Who was the first Chief Justice of the U.S. Supreme Court?
John Jay

ANATOMY (2)
True or false?
The small intestine is longer than the large intestine.

EARTH SCIENCE (3)
In the Southern Hemisphere, the vernal equinox occurs in which month?
September

ENGLISH (4)
An example of an oxymoron is:
A) peanut gallery
B) rhyme time
C) living dead

GOVERNMENT (5)
True or false? The President and Vice President live in the White House.

Your Score:

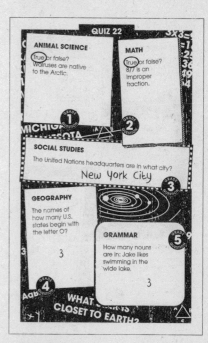

QUIZ 22

ANIMAL SCIENCE (1)
True or false?
Walruses are native to the Arctic.

MATH (2)
True or false?
877 is an improper fraction.

SOCIAL STUDIES (3)
The United Nations headquarters are in what city?
New York City

GEOGRAPHY (4)
The names of how many U.S. states begin with the letter O?
3

GRAMMAR (5)
How many nouns are in: Jake likes swimming in the wide lake.
3

Your Score:

ANSWERS

QUIZ 23

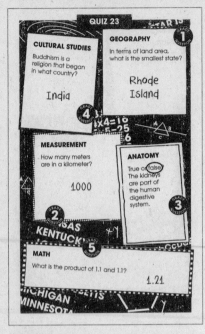

CULTURAL STUDIES

Buddhism is a religion that began in what country?

India

GEOGRAPHY

In terms of land area, what is the smallest state?

Rhode Island

MEASUREMENT

How many meters are in a kilometer?

1000

ANATOMY

True or false? The kidneys are part of the human digestive system.

MATH

What is the product of 1.1 and 1.1?

1.21

Your Score: _____

QUIZ 24

GEOGRAPHY

Russia's longest land border is with what other country?

Kazakhstan

MATH

How many sides are there on a trapezoid?

4

SCIENCE

True or false? A spider is an insect.

U.S. STUDIES

What is the capital of Massachusetts?

Boston

GRAMMAR

What is the verb in: It is such a nice day!

is

Your Score: _____

QUIZ 25

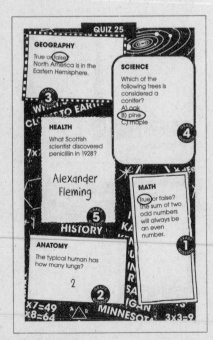

GEOGRAPHY

True or false? North America is in the Eastern Hemisphere.

SCIENCE

Which of the following trees is considered a conifer?
A) oak
B) pine
C) maple

HEALTH

What Scottish scientist discovered penicillin in 1928?

Alexander Fleming

MATH

True or false? The sum of two odd numbers will always be an even number.

ANATOMY

The typical human has how many lungs?

2

Your Score: _____

QUIZ 26

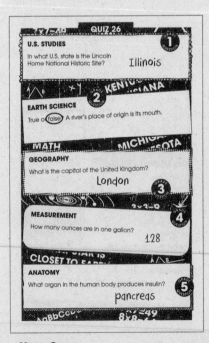

U.S. STUDIES

In what U.S. state is the Lincoln Home National Historic Site?

Illinois

EARTH SCIENCE

True or false? A river's place of origin is its mouth.

GEOGRAPHY

What is the capital of the United Kingdom?

London

MEASUREMENT

How many ounces are in one gallon?

128

ANATOMY

What organ in the human body produces insulin?

pancreas

Your Score: _____

ANSWERS

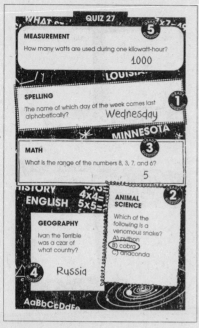

QUIZ 27 — Grade 5

MEASUREMENT
How many watts are used during one kilowatt-hour?
1000

SPELLING — Grade 1
The name of which day of the week comes last alphabetically?
Wednesday

MATH — Grade 3
What is the range of the numbers 8, 3, 7, and 6?
5

GEOGRAPHY — Grade 4
Ivan the Terrible was a czar of what country?
Russia

ANIMAL SCIENCE — Grade 2
Which of the following is a venomous snake?
A) python
B) cobra
C) anaconda

Your Score:

QUIZ 28

MATH — Grade 4
What is the product of 4/5 and 125?
100

MUSIC — Grade 5
The two most common clefs used in modern music are the treble and what other clef?
bass

SPELLING — Grade 2
What month comes last alphabetically?
September

ANIMAL SCIENCE — Grade 3
True or false? The Alaskan malamute is a species of fish.
false

ENGLISH — Grade 1
How many apostrophes are missing from: Nathans dog licked its paw.
one

Your Score:

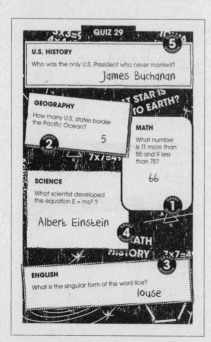

QUIZ 29 — Grade 5

U.S. HISTORY
Who was the only U.S. President who never married?
James Buchanan

GEOGRAPHY — Grade 2
How many U.S. states border the Pacific Ocean?
5

MATH
What number is 11 more than 55 and 9 less than 75?
66

SCIENCE — Grade 1
What scientist developed the equation $E = mc^2$?
Albert Einstein

ENGLISH — Grade 3
What is the singular form of the word lice?
louse

Your Score:

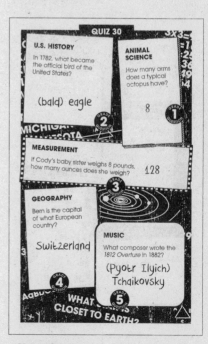

QUIZ 30

U.S. HISTORY — Grade 2
In 1782, what became the official bird of the United States?
(bald) eagle

ANIMAL SCIENCE — Grade 1
How many arms does a typical octopus have?
8

MEASUREMENT — Grade 3
If Cody's baby sister weighs 8 pounds, how many ounces does she weigh?
128

GEOGRAPHY — Grade 4
Bern is the capital of what European country?
Switzerland

MUSIC — Grade 5
What composer wrote the 1812 Overture in 1882?
(Pyotr Ilyich) Tchaikovsky

Your Score:

ANSWERS

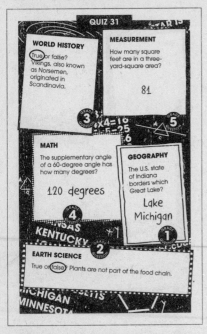

QUIZ 31

WORLD HISTORY
(True) or false?
Vikings, also known
as Norsemen,
originated in
Scandinavia.

3

MEASUREMENT
How many square
feet are in a three-
yard-square area?

81

5

MATH
The supplementary angle
of a 60-degree angle has
how many degrees?

120 degrees

4

GEOGRAPHY
The U.S. state
of Indiana
borders which
Great Lake?

Lake
Michigan

1

2

EARTH SCIENCE
True or (false?) Plants are not part of the food chain.

Your Score:

QUIZ 32

HEALTH
How many canine
teeth are in a typical
adult human mouth?

4

4

ANIMAL SCIENCE
True or (false?) The
wolverine is a
member of the
canine family.

2

5

EARTH SCIENCE
Coal and diamonds are made of what element?

carbon

MEASUREMENT
Of the current U.S.
coins, which is
smallest in size?

dime

1

P.E.
To the nearest mile, how
long is a standard
Olympic marathon?

26 miles

3

Your Score:

QUIZ 33

MATH
What whole number
is the closest to the
square root of 50?

7

4

GEOGRAPHY
Yosemite National Park
is located in what U.S.
state?

California

2

BIOLOGY
A typical amoeba
has how many
cells?

one

3

ASTRONOMY
What was the
name of the first
American
woman to travel
into outer
space?

Sally
Ride

5

1

EARTH SCIENCE
True or (false?) Lightning is a
form of precipitation.

Your Score:

QUIZ 34

U.S. STUDIES
How many U.S. states have the word North,
South, East, or West in their names?

5

2

5

MEASUREMENT
In the U.S., how many pounds are in a ton?

2000

GEOGRAPHY
What is the capital of Brazil?

Brasília

4

MATH
At 48 cents a pound, how much does
5/8 of a pound of peanuts cost?

30 cents

3

LITERATURE
In folklore, what is the name of Paul Bunyan's blue ox?

Babe

1

Your Score:

ANSWERS

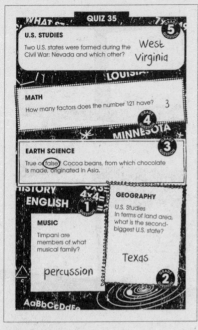

QUIZ 35
5

U.S. STUDIES
Two U.S. states were formed during the Civil War: Nevada and which other? — **West Virginia**

MATH
How many factors does the number 121 have? — **3** — 4

EARTH SCIENCE
True or (false?) Cocoa beans, from which chocolate is made, originated in Asia. — 3

ENGLISH — 1

MUSIC
Timpani are members of what musical family? — **percussion**

GEOGRAPHY
U.S. Studies
In terms of land area, what is the second-biggest U.S. state? — **Texas** — 2

Your Score:

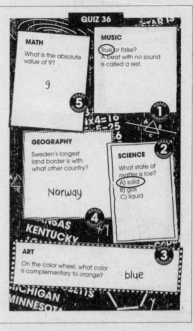

QUIZ 36

MATH
What is the absolute value of 9? — **9** — 5

MUSIC
(True) or false? A beat with no sound is called a rest. — 1

GEOGRAPHY
Sweden's longest land border is with what other country? — **Norway** — 4

SCIENCE
What state of matter is ice?
A) solid
B) gas
C) liquid — 2

ART
On the color wheel, what color is complementary to orange? — **blue** — 3

Your Score:

QUIZ 37
1

MATH
True or (false?) The sum of the digits in the number 768 is equal to 22.

CHEMISTRY
What is the lightest noble gas? — **helium** — 5

ENGLISH
"Wept" is the past tense form of what verb? — **(to) weep** — 3

GEOGRAPHY
The Allegheny and Monongahela rivers meet and form the Ohio River in what U.S. city? — **Pittsburgh, Pennsylvania**

SPELLING
The plural form of the word "quiz" has how many letters? — **7** — 2

Your Score:

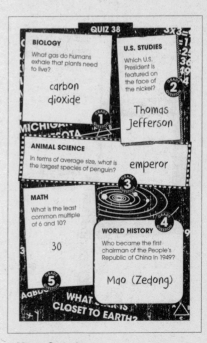

QUIZ 38

BIOLOGY
What gas do humans exhale that plants need to live? — **carbon dioxide** — 1

U.S. STUDIES
Which U.S. President is featured on the face of the nickel? — **Thomas Jefferson** — 2

ANIMAL SCIENCE
In terms of average size, what is the largest species of penguin? — **emperor** — 3

MATH
What is the least common multiple of 6 and 10? — **30** — 4

WORLD HISTORY
Who became the first chairman of the People's Republic of China in 1949? — **Mao (Zedong)** — 5

Your Score:

ANSWERS

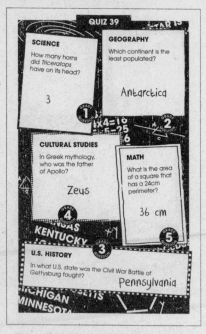

QUIZ 39

SCIENCE
How many horns did *Triceratops* have on its head?

3

GEOGRAPHY
Which continent is the least populated?

Antarctica

CULTURAL STUDIES
In Greek mythology, who was the father of Apollo?

Zeus

MATH
What is the area of a square that has a 24cm perimeter?

36 cm

U.S. HISTORY
In what U.S. state was the Civil War Battle of Gettysburg fought?

Pennsylvania

Your Score:

QUIZ 40

BIOLOGY
An animal without a backbone is an:
A) invertebrate
B) arthropod
C) amphibian

U.S. HISTORY
What U.S. President only served one month in office?

William Harrison

LITERATURE
In Homer's *Odyssey*, the monster Cyclops has how many eyes?

one

CULTURAL STUDIES
The holiday Cinco de Mayo originated in what country?

Mexico

ASTRONOMY
How many confirmed planets (as of October 2016) are in our solar system?

8

Your Score:

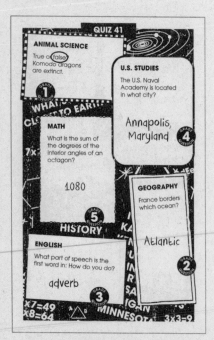

QUIZ 41

ANIMAL SCIENCE
True or false? Komodo dragons are extinct.

U.S. STUDIES
The U.S. Naval Academy is located in what city?

Annapolis, Maryland

MATH
What is the sum of the degrees of the interior angles of an octagon?

1080

GEOGRAPHY
France borders which ocean?

Atlantic

ENGLISH
What part of speech is the first word in: How do you do?

adverb

Your Score:

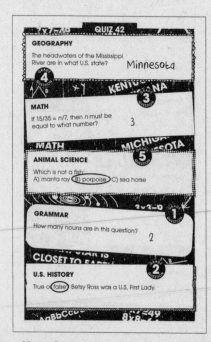

QUIZ 42

GEOGRAPHY
The headwaters of the Mississippi River are in what U.S. state?

Minnesota

MATH
If $15/35 = n/7$, then n must be equal to what number?

3

ANIMAL SCIENCE
Which is not a fish?
A) manta ray B) porpoise C) sea horse

GRAMMAR
How many nouns are in this question?

2

U.S. HISTORY
True or false? Betsy Ross was a U.S. First Lady.

Your Score:

ANSWERS

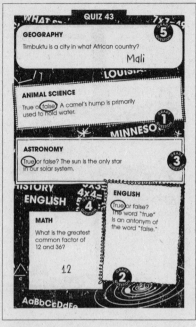

QUIZ 43

GEOGRAPHY
Timbuktu is a city in what African country?

Mali

ANIMAL SCIENCE
True or (false) A camel's hump is primarily used to hold water.

ASTRONOMY
(True) or false? The sun is the only star in our solar system.

ENGLISH
(True) or false? The word "true" is an antonym of the word "false."

MATH
What is the greatest common factor of 12 and 36?

12

Your Score:

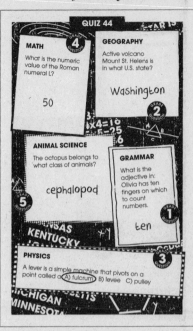

QUIZ 44

MATH
What is the numeric value of the Roman numeral L?

50

GEOGRAPHY
Active volcano Mount St. Helens is in what U.S. state?

Washington

ANIMAL SCIENCE
The octopus belongs to what class of animals?

cephalopod

GRAMMAR
What is the adjective in: Olivia has ten fingers on which to count numbers.

ten

PHYSICS
A lever is a simple machine that pivots on a point called a (A) fulcrum B) levee C) pulley

Your Score:

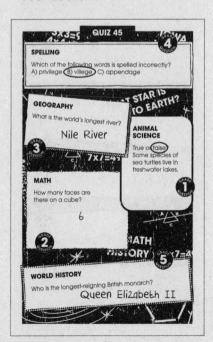

QUIZ 45

SPELLING
Which of the following words is spelled incorrectly?
A) privilege (B) villege C) appendage

GEOGRAPHY
What is the world's longest river?

Nile River

ANIMAL SCIENCE
True or (false) Some species of sea turtles live in freshwater lakes.

MATH
How many faces are there on a cube?

6

WORLD HISTORY
Who is the longest-reigning British monarch?

Queen Elizabeth II

Your Score:

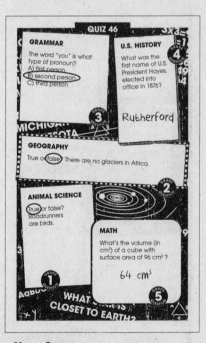

QUIZ 46

GRAMMAR
The word "you" is what type of pronoun?
A) first person
(B) second person)
C) third person

U.S. HISTORY
What was the first name of U.S. President Hayes, elected into office in 1876?

Rutherford

GEOGRAPHY
True or (false) There are no glaciers in Africa.

ANIMAL SCIENCE
(True) or false? Roadrunners are birds.

MATH
What's the volume (in cm³) of a cube with surface area of 96 cm²?

64 cm³

Your Score:

ANSWERS

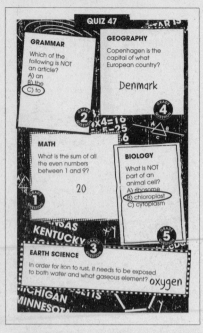

QUIZ 47

GRAMMAR
Which of the following is NOT an article?
A) an
B) the
C) to ✓

GEOGRAPHY
Copenhagen is the capital of what European country?

Denmark

MATH
What is the sum of all the even numbers between 1 and 9?

20

BIOLOGY
What is NOT part of an animal cell?
A) ribosome
B) chloroplast ✓
C) cytoplasm

EARTH SCIENCE
In order for iron to rust, it needs to be exposed to both water and what gaseous element? oxygen

Your Score:

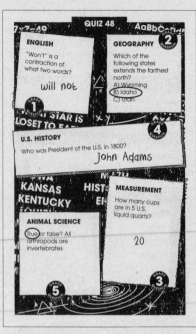

QUIZ 48

ENGLISH
"Won't" is a contraction of what two words?

will not

GEOGRAPHY
Which of the following states extends the farthest north?
A) Wyoming
B) Idaho ✓
C) Utah

U.S. HISTORY
Who was President of the U.S. in 1800?

John Adams

MEASUREMENT
How many cups are in 5 U.S. liquid quarts?

20

ANIMAL SCIENCE
True ✓ or false? All arthropods are invertebrates

Your Score:

QUIZ 49

ANIMAL SCIENCE
True ✓ or false? A chimpanzee has no tail.

PHYSICS
Radio frequency AM: the A stands for amplitude; the M stands for what?

modulation

GEOGRAPHY
Dormant volcano Mount Hood is located in what U.S. state?

Oregon

ENGLISH
Which is punctuated correctly:
A) 'Tis II
B) Tis II
C) 'Tis II ✓

U.S. HISTORY
The thirteen American Colonies gained independence from what country?

Great Britain (England)

Your Score:

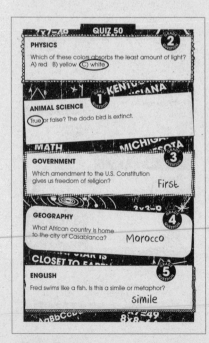

QUIZ 50

PHYSICS
Which of these colors absorbs the least amount of light?
A) red B) yellow C) white ✓

ANIMAL SCIENCE
True ✓ or false? The dodo bird is extinct.

GOVERNMENT
Which amendment to the U.S. Constitution gives us freedom of religion?

First

GEOGRAPHY
What African country is home to the city of Casablanca?

Morocco

ENGLISH
Fred swims like a fish. Is this a simile or metaphor?

simile

Your Score:

ANSWERS

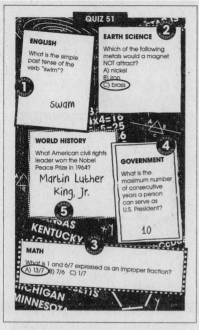

QUIZ 51

ENGLISH
What is the simple past tense of the verb "swim"?

swam

EARTH SCIENCE
Which of the following metals would a magnet NOT attract?
A) nickel
B) iron
C) brass ⟵

WORLD HISTORY
What American civil rights leader won the Nobel Peace Prize in 1964?

Martin Luther King, Jr.

GOVERNMENT
What is the maximum number of consecutive years a person can serve as U.S. President?

10

MATH
What is 1 and 6/7 expressed as an improper fraction?
A) 13/7 ⟵ B) 7/6 C) 1/7

Your Score:

QUIZ 52

GEOGRAPHY
The mouth of the Indus river is in what country?

Pakistan

ANIMAL SCIENCE
True or false?
The Japanese giant salamander is warm-blooded.

ENGLISH
What is the last consonant in the modern English alphabet?

Z

ASTRONOMY
What galaxy is closest in distance to the Milky Way?

Andromeda

MATH
True or false?
When you divide 30 by 4, there is no remainder.

Your Score:

QUIZ 53

BIOLOGY
True or false?
The cicada is a type of insect.

U.S. HISTORY
Who was elected president of the Confederate States during the American Civil War?

Jefferson Davis

MATH
Sierra had 30 cookies for her party. All nine kids at the party ate two cookies each. How many were left over?

12

ART
In weaving, the vertical and horizontal threads are called the warp and the:
A) wane
B) weft ⟵
C) loop

EARTH SCIENCE
Acorns come from what species of tree?

oak

Your Score:

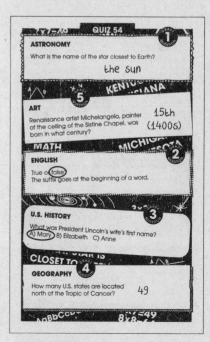

QUIZ 54

ASTRONOMY
What is the name of the star closest to Earth?

the sun

ART
Renaissance artist Michelangelo, painter of the ceiling of the Sistine Chapel, was born in what century?

15th (1400s)

ENGLISH
True or false?
The suffix goes at the beginning of a word.

U.S. HISTORY
What was President Lincoln's wife's first name?
A) Mary ⟵ B) Elizabeth C) Anne

GEOGRAPHY
How many U.S. states are located north of the Tropic of Cancer?

49

Your Score:

ANSWERS

QUIZ 55

ASTRONOMY
Our moon is in orbit around
A) the sun B) the night sky C) Earth

NUTRITION
Fuji and Gala are both varieties of what fruit?
apple

GEOGRAPHY
Which of the seven continents has the largest population?
Asia

PHYSICS
32° Fahrenheit is equal to what degree Celsius?
0° (zero)

MATH
What is the sum of 11.5 and negative 14?
-2.5

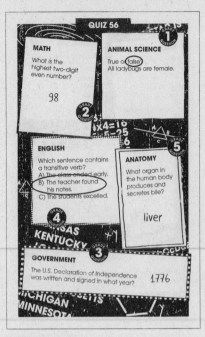

QUIZ 56

MATH
What is the highest two-digit even number?
98

ANIMAL SCIENCE
True or false?
All ladybugs are female.

ENGLISH
Which sentence contains a transitive verb?
A) The class ended early.
B) The teacher found his notes.
C) The students excelled.

ANATOMY
What organ in the human body produces and secretes bile?
liver

GOVERNMENT
The U.S. Declaration of Independence was written and signed in what year?
1776

Your Score:

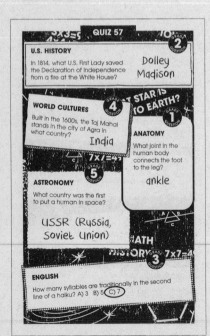

QUIZ 57

U.S. HISTORY
In 1814, what U.S. First Lady saved the Declaration of Independence from a fire at the White House?
Dolley Madison

WORLD CULTURES
Built in the 1600s, the Taj Mahal stands in the city of Agra in what country?
India

ANATOMY
What joint in the human body connects the foot to the leg?
ankle

ASTRONOMY
What country was the first to put a human in space?
USSR (Russia, Soviet Union)

ENGLISH
How many syllables are traditionally in the second line of a haiku? A) 3 B) 5 C) 7

Your Score:

QUIZ 58

PHYSICS
Which of the following is measured in units known as nektons?
A) force
B) mass
C) heat

ANATOMY
True or false?
The epidermis is directly underneath the dermis.

U.S. STUDIES
Which U.S. President is featured on the face of the dime?
Franklin Roosevelt

ANIMAL SCIENCE
True or false?
A tick is an arachnid.

ENGLISH
True or false?
The plural of "roof" is "rooves."

Your Score:

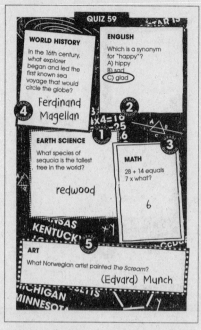

QUIZ 59

WORLD HISTORY

In the 16th century, what explorer began and led the first known sea voyage that would circle the globe?

Ferdinand Magellan

ENGLISH

Which is a synonym for "happy"?
A) hippy
B) sad
C) glad

EARTH SCIENCE

What species of sequoia is the tallest tree in the world?

redwood

MATH

28 + 14 equals 7 x what?

6

ART

What Norwegian artist painted *The Scream*?

(Edvard) Munch

Your Score:

QUIZ 60

WORLD CULTURES

Which is NOT an official language of Switzerland?
A) German
B) Italian
C) Swedish

MATH

If the sum of negative 4 and positive 6 is y, then how much is y times 3?

6

ENGLISH

True or false? A complete simple sentence must always contain at least one verb.

ASTRONOMY

In the sun's core, hydrogen atoms fuse together to form what other element?

helium

GOVERNMENT

A U.S. Supreme Court Justice is appointed to serve for how long?
A) 4 years
B) 20 years
C) lifetime appointment

Your Score:

QUIZ 61

U.S. STUDIES

True or false? If you are born in the U.S. (to non-diplomats), then you are an American citizen.

ANIMAL SCIENCE

True or false? Horses can sleep standing up.

GOVERNMENT

Can a person born in Germany to an American-citizen mother later qualify to become President of the U.S.?

yes

ASTRONOMY

More than 99% of the mass of our solar system is contained within what heavenly body?

the sun

MATH

If Olivia ran 36 miles in 4 hours, on average how many miles did she run per hour?

9 mph

Your Score:

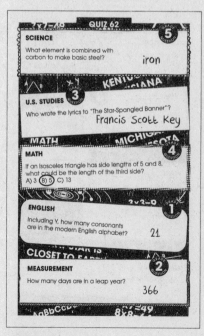

QUIZ 62

SCIENCE

What element is combined with carbon to make basic steel?

iron

U.S. STUDIES

Who wrote the lyrics to "The Star-Spangled Banner"?

Francis Scott Key

MATH

If an isosceles triangle has side lengths of 5 and 8, what could be the length of the third side?
A) 3 B) 5 C) 13

ENGLISH

Including Y, how many consonants are in the modern English alphabet?

21

MEASUREMENT

How many days are in a leap year?

366

Your Score:

ANSWERS

QUIZ 63

4

ASTRONOMY
What is the brightest star we can see in the night sky?
Sirius (the Dog Star)

2

BIOLOGY
How many legs does a butterfly have?
6

5

GEOGRAPHY
What U.S. state is home to Acadia National Park?
Maine

3

ART
What 16th-century artist painted the *Mona Lisa*?
Leonardo da Vinci

1

ENGLISH
How many syllables are in the word "syllable"?
3

Your Score:

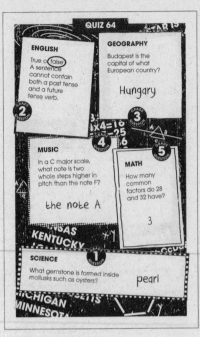

QUIZ 64

2

ENGLISH
True or false
A sentence cannot contain both a past tense and a future tense verb.

GEOGRAPHY
Budapest is the capital of what European country?
Hungary

4

MUSIC
In a C major scale, what note is two whole steps higher in pitch than the note F?
the note A

5

MATH
How many common factors do 28 and 32 have?
3

1

SCIENCE
What gemstone is formed inside mollusks such as oysters?
pearl

Your Score:

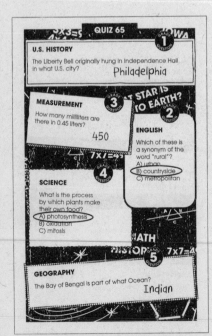

QUIZ 65

1

U.S. HISTORY
The Liberty Bell originally hung in Independence Hall in what U.S. city?
Philadelphia

3

MEASUREMENT
How many milliliters are there in 0.45 liters?
450

2

ENGLISH
Which of these is a synonym of the word "rural"?
A) urban
B) countryside
C) metropolitan

4

SCIENCE
What is the process by which plants make their own food?
A) photosynthesis
B) oxidation
C) mitosis

5

GEOGRAPHY
The Bay of Bengal is part of what Ocean?
Indian

Your Score:

QUIZ 66

2

GEOGRAPHY
Puget Sound is a body of water bordered by what U.S. state?
Washington

ANIMAL SCIENCE
True or false
Giant pandas hibernate.

1

VOCABULARY
By definition, how many wheels does a unicycle have?
one

4

PHYSICS
Which refers to the lowest point of a sound wave?
A) crest
B) trough
C) period

5

U.S. HISTORY
U.S. President John Adams was a member of what political party at the time of his election?
Federalist

3

Your Score:

ANSWERS

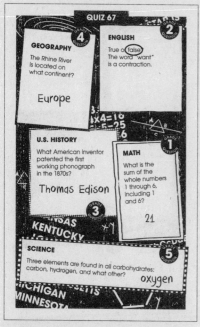

QUIZ 67

GEOGRAPHY
The Rhine River is located on what continent?

Europe

ENGLISH
True or false?
The word "want" is a contraction.

U.S. HISTORY
What American inventor patented the first working phonograph in the 1870s?

Thomas Edison

MATH
What is the sum of the whole numbers 1 through 6, including 1 and 6?

21

SCIENCE
Three elements are found in all carbohydrates: carbon, hydrogen, and what other?

oxygen

Your Score:

QUIZ 68

SCIENCE
True or false?
The positively charged ends of two magnets will attract each other.

GEOGRAPHY
What is the fourth most populous country, after China, India, and the U.S.?

Indonesia

MATH
What is the simplest form of the fraction 18/81?

2/9

ENGLISH
Which is a homophone of the word "night"?
A) knight
B) day
C) evening

MUSIC
Cymbals belong to what musical family?

percussion

Your Score:

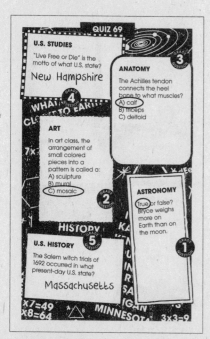

QUIZ 69

U.S. STUDIES
"Live Free or Die" is the motto of what U.S. state?

New Hampshire

ANATOMY
The Achilles tendon connects the heel bone to what muscles?
A) calf
B) triceps
C) deltoid

ART
In art class, the arrangement of small colored pieces into a pattern is called a:
A) sculpture
B) mural
C) mosaic

ASTRONOMY
True or false?
Bryce weighs more on Earth than on the moon.

U.S. HISTORY
The Salem witch trials of 1692 occurred in what present-day U.S. state?

Massachusetts

Your Score:

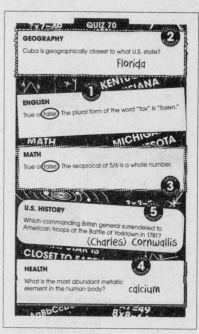

QUIZ 70

GEOGRAPHY
Cuba is geographically closest to what U.S. state?

Florida

ENGLISH
True or false? The plural form of the word "fox" is "foxen."

MATH
True or false? The reciprocal of 5/6 is a whole number.

U.S. HISTORY
Which commanding British general surrendered to American troops at the Battle of Yorktown in 1781?

(Charles) Cornwallis

HEALTH
What is the most abundant metallic element in the human body?

calcium

Your Score:

ANSWERS

QUIZ 71

HEALTH — GRADE 3
(True) or false? Someone who is nearsighted has trouble seeing things far away.

SCIENCE — GRADE 1
(True) or false?
Pollen is part of a plant's reproductive system.

GEOGRAPHY — GRADE 2
Omaha is the most populous city in what U.S. state?
Nebraska

U.S. HISTORY — GRADE 4
On Dec. 1, 1955, Rosa Parks famously refused to give up her seat on a bus in what U.S. city?
Montgomery, Alabama

ENGLISH — GRADE 5
From the Greek meaning "outermost line of verse," what type of poem has letters at the beginning of each line that spell out a message?
acrostic

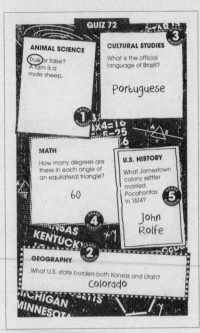

QUIZ 72

ANIMAL SCIENCE — GRADE 1
(True) or false?
A ram is a male sheep.

CULTURAL STUDIES — GRADE 3
What is the official language of Brazil?
Portuguese

MATH — GRADE 4
How many degrees are there in each angle of an equilateral triangle?
60

U.S. HISTORY — GRADE 5
What Jamestown colony settler married Pocahontas in 1614?
John Rolfe

GEOGRAPHY — GRADE 2
What U.S. state borders both Kansas and Utah?
Colorado

Your Score:

QUIZ 73

U.S. HISTORY — GRADE 1
What was the first name of the first U.S. First Lady?
Martha

U.S. STUDIES — GRADE 3
What is the capital of Arkansas?
Little Rock

ANIMAL SCIENCE — GRADE 2
(True) or false?
All roosters are male.

CULTURAL STUDIES — GRADE 4
What day of the week is named after the Norse god of thunder?
Thursday (Thor's day)

GEOGRAPHY — GRADE 5
What is the largest of the Mariana Islands in the western Pacific Ocean?
Guam

Your Score:

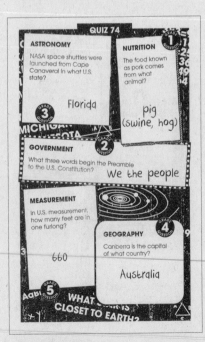

QUIZ 74

ASTRONOMY — GRADE 3
NASA space shuttles were launched from Cape Canaveral in what U.S. state?
Florida

NUTRITION — GRADE 1
The food known as pork comes from what animal?
pig (swine, hog)

GOVERNMENT — GRADE 2
What three words begin the Preamble to the U.S. Constitution?
We the people

MEASUREMENT — GRADE 5
In U.S. measurement, how many feet are in one furlong?
660

GEOGRAPHY — GRADE 4
Canberra is the capital of what country?
Australia

Your Score: